CRAIG DAVID. SLICKER THAN YOUR AVERAGE

THIS PUBLICATION IS NOT AUTHORISED
FOR SALE IN THE UNITED STATES OF AMERICA
AND / OR CANADA

WISE PUBLICATIONS
LONDON / NEW YORK / PARIS / SYDNEY /
COPENHAGEN / BERLIN / MADRID / TOKYO

EXCLUSIVE DISTRIBUTORS:
MUSIC SALES LIMITED
8/9 FRITH STREET, LONDON W1D 3JB, ENGLAND.
MUSIC SALES PTY LIMITED
120 ROTHSCHILD AVENUE, ROSEBERY, NSW 2018, AUSTRALIA.

ORDER NO. AM976217
ISBN 0-7119-9791-8
THIS BOOK © COPYRIGHT 2003 BY WISE PUBLICATIONS.

MUSIC ARRANGEMENTS BY DEREK JONES.
MUSIC PROCESSED BY PAUL EWERS MUSIC DESIGN.

PRINTED IN THE UNITED KINGDOM BY
PRINTWISE (HAVERHILL) LIMITED, SUFFOLK

WWW.MUSICSALES.COM

YOUR GUARANTEE OF QUALITY:

AS PUBLISHERS, WE STRIVE TO PRODUCE EVERY BOOK
TO THE HIGHEST COMMERCIAL STANDARDS.

WHILE ENDEAVOURING TO RETAIN THE ORIGINAL RUNNING
ORDER OF THE RECORDED ALBUM, THE BOOK HAS BEEN
CAREFULLY DESIGNED TO MINIMISE AWKWARD PAGE TURNS
AND TO MAKE PLAYING FROM IT A REAL PLEASURE.

PARTICULAR CARE HAS BEEN GIVEN TO SPECIFYING
ACID-FREE, NEUTRAL-SIZED PAPER MADE FROM PULPS WHICH
HAVE NOT BEEN ELEMENTAL CHLORINE BLEACHED.

THIS PULP IS FROM FARMED SUSTAINABLE FORESTS AND
WAS PRODUCED WITH SPECIAL REGARD FOR THE ENVIRONMENT.

THROUGHOUT, THE PRINTING AND BINDING HAVE BEEN
PLANNED TO ENSURE A STURDY, ATTRACTIVE PUBLICATION
WHICH SHOULD GIVE YEARS OF ENJOYMENT.

IF YOUR COPY FAILS TO MEET OUR HIGH STANDARDS,
PLEASE INFORM US AND WE WILL GLADLY REPLACE IT.

SLICKER THAN YOUR AVERAGE

WORDS & MUSIC BY CRAIG DAVID, TREVOR HENRY & ANTHONY MARSHALL

There comes a time when you got-ta take a stand to do what's right. As much as I like I can't pos-si-bly please ev-'ry-one. Ooh.

Slick-er than your av-'rage sing-er serv-ing ga-rage, bu-sy tryin' to slam me 'cause I smashed it.

9

Now to go gold to me's a mi-ni-mal, I'm in-volved in them plat-inum plaques and re-cords sold. Hea-ven

knows that I've bat-tled pro-duc-ers with e-gos and there were those that were told ex-act-ly where to go.

Some-bo-dy please stop_ these lit-tle kids that wan-na pull bump-ers of__ my 2 0 6,

shout-ing out-side of the block I used to live. They don't like my re-cords so why lis-ten to this?

11

WHAT'S YOUR FLAVA?

WORDS & MUSIC BY CRAIG DAVID, TREVOR HENRY & ANTHONY MARSHALL

What's your fla - va? Tell me what's_ your fla - va? What's your fla - va?

Tell me what's_ your fla - va? What's your fla - va? Tell me what's_ your fla - va?

What's your fla - va? Tell me what's_ your fla - va?

Fm⁷ Fm⁶ Fm⁷

What's your fla - va? Tell me what's__ your fla - va?

Fm⁶ B♭m/F F⁵

What's your fla - va? Tell me what's__ your fla - va?

B♭sus⁴/F

What's your fla - va? Tell me what's__ your fla - va?

repeat as instrumental after 2nd Verse

B♭/F B♭m/F F⁵

What's your fla - va? Tell me what's__ your fla - va?

15

2. I take 'em in the mid - dle of Ju - ly with the drop top down in the park when it's sum - mer - ing
3. I'm tak - ing 'em apple and cin - na - mon girls I'm feel - in 'em can't stop lick - in 'em,

these ice - creams look - ing so fly that I just can't lie it all seems too be - wild - er - ing.
that's why they got me drib - bl - ing hot fudge sauce and it's all ov - er my Tim - ber - lands.

They got these grown men run - ning 'round,
I take these them car - a - mel with a hint

scream - ing out, act - ing worse than child - ren but who
of van - i - lla with a lit - tle choc - 'late sprin - kl - ings

18

FAST CARS

WORDS & MUSIC BY CRAIG DAVID, TREVOR HENRY & ANTHONY MARSHALL

way that you purr___ at me, you know you pre-fer___ the speed.
When your

back starts dip-ping.
{ Wheels spin-ning when the gears start shift-ing. I'm stick-ing 'til the
{ And I'm un-a-ware of the li-mits I'm hit-ting. Blurred vi - sion and a

tur-bo kicks in. You know_ that I'm mis-sing, got me mov-ing so fast you got me miss-ing the flash of five
cri-ti-cal con-di-tion could blow the trans-mis-sion, got me mov-ing so fast you got me miss-ing the flash of five

O! } Fast cars, fast wo-men, speed bikes with ni - tro in 'em.
O! }

Dan - ger - ous when driv - en. Those are the types that I be feel - ing.

Fast cars, fast wo - men, speed bikes with ni - tro in 'em.

1.

Dan - ger - ous when driv - en. Those are the types that I be feel - ing.

2.

N.C.

Those are the types that I be feel - ing.

HIDDEN AGENDA

WORDS & MUSIC BY CRAIG DAVID & MARK HILL

SPANISH

WORDS & MUSIC BY CRAIG DAVID, TREVOR HENRY & ANTHONY MARSHALL

Would you like a drink with me?

(If you don't mind, can I

You know that you don't have to leave say - ing
touch - ing ca - ress - ing.) (To - night)

why did-n't I go home with you to -
Would you like a

why did-n't I go home with you to -

-night.

Repeat to fade

41

EENIE MEENIE

WORDS & MUSIC BY CRAIG DAVID, TREVOR HENRY, LEROY WILLIAMS & ADAM LYONS

way home, hap - py 'cause I'm gon - na see my girl___ to - night.
ac - cess to the vi - sa, the keys to the flat, wide - screen TV, DVD's and that.

Some - thing mess - ing with my ra - dio, got - ta be___ my
All of a sud - den you be trip-pin' when I ans-wer the phone, talk-ing all a - bout me in an an - gry tone,

cell phone___ ring - ing.___
talk - ing all a - bout how I be do - ing you wrong, you're cra - zy.

I picked it up, it was my girl - friend, but she would - n't talk___
What - ev - er hap - pened to the good girl?

1° Only

44

Ee - nie mee - nie mi - nie mo, get - ting kind - a cri - ti - cal. Don't wan - na hurt you though but I got - ta let you go.

Ee - nie mee - nie mi - nie mo, gon - na miss you that I know. Girl it's been won - der - ful, but I got - ta let you go.

To Coda ⊕ N.C.

Ee - nie mee - nie mi - nie mo, get - ting kind - a cri - ti - cal. Don't wan - na hurt you though.

You know what, well I'm just an or - din - 'ry guy,____ deal - ing with ru - mours and lies.____

But your friends keep on fill - ing your head__ with this non - sense and I__ can't take__ no more.__

Craig Da - vid, she on - ly af - ter that wage pay - slip that's why she got you pull - ing
digger degree she must've studied for that, wanted me to get her a mansion with a truck in the back.
You give them an inch and they be taking the piss, you fed up of it get rid of the witch, don't be taking her shit.

strange fa - ces. Drink - ing Hen - nes - sey 'til your brain's was - ted. She don't wan - na be the girl that
Flood her with ice 'til a nigger like honey relax Messiah bolical ain't even got no money for that.
She wasn't saying this when he was licking her lower lip making her throw a fit, put your fingers all over it.

Craig stays with. She just wan - na be there while Craig stays rich. She would - n't be with him if he was
All of a sudden you be tripping on my cellular phone, talking about all of the women that be taking me home.
Tripping all over you whenever you rock the show, trying to get money 'cause she know you got the dough.

47

YOU DON'T MISS YOUR WATER
('TIL THE WELL RUNS DRY)

WORDS & MUSIC BY CRAIG DAVID & MARK HILL

RISE & FALL

WORDS & MUSIC BY CRAIG DAVID, STING & DOMINIC MILLER

63

PERSONAL

WORDS & MUSIC BY CRAIG DAVID, TREVOR HENRY,
ANTHONY MARSHALL, JAMIE FOXX & BILLY MOSS

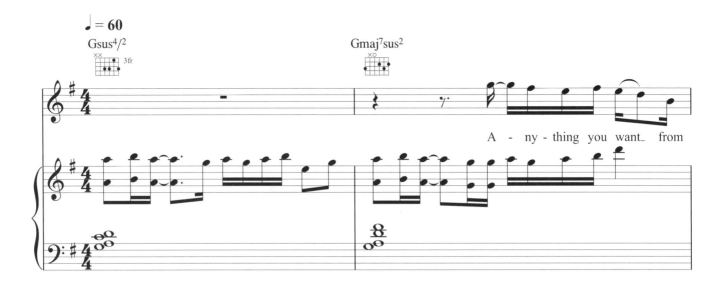

2.

love to head to your bed so that we can get per - son - al,___

should I take off my clothes? (No) Put the lock on the door? Let go of your

deep - est in - hi - bi - tions, let me ful - fil your fan - ta - sy, girl.___

___ Like me touch - ing you there? (Yeah) The way that I play with your hair?___ E -

69

HANDS UP IN THE AIR
WORDS & MUSIC BY CRAIG DAVID & MARK HILL

Yeah, yeah.___ This one___ goes out to all my fel-las,___ all my la-dies, ah,

yeah,___ ah, yeah.___ Now I know it's kin-da ea-sy to raise the roof with your crew yeah.___ Al-

-right,___ al-right.___Ooh, but I know it ain't that ea-sy___ to bring the whole thing___ down.___

Let me see those hands up in the air, all my fel-las boun-cing in the club let me hear you say yeah.___

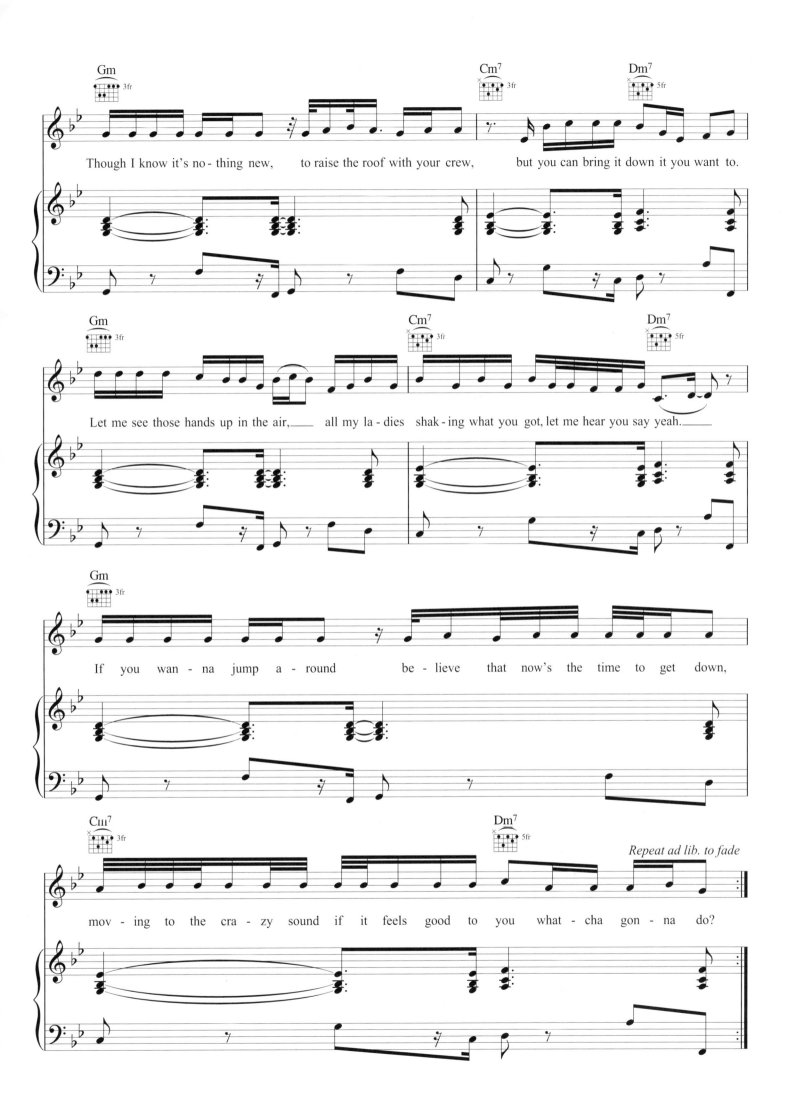

Though I know it's no - thing new, to raise the roof with your crew, but you can bring it down it you want to.

Let me see those hands up in the air,___ all my la - dies shak - ing what you got, let me hear you say yeah.___

If you wan - na jump a - round be - lieve that now's the time to get down,

Repeat ad lib. to fade

mov - ing to the cra - zy sound if it feels good to you what - cha gon - na do?

2 STEPS BACK

WORDS & MUSIC BY CRAIG DAVID, CARSTEN SCHACK, KENNETH KARLIN,
JIMMY COZIER, NATE BUTLER & HAROLD LILLY

left back. oh._____ Girl, you real - ly ought to think a - bout_ it

'cause there's real - ly no doubt a - bout_ it, you know I've been there for you_ and

1, 2. that's the truth. Ev - 'ry time we take **3.** that's the truth.

N.C.

N.C. *Repeat ad lib. to fade*

Ev - er - y time._____

Drums

WORLD FILLED WITH LOVE

WORDS & MUSIC BY CRAIG DAVID & FRASER SMITH

WHAT'S CHANGED

WORDS & MUSIC BY CRAIG DAVID & MARK HILL

Hey, ba - by.___ Oh,___ tell___

___ me___ Craig,___ why_ d'ya wan - na___ play_ these_ games with me?___Thought you

al - ways want - ed to be with me. Well at first girl, I want - ed to.___ But things have changed

find my way_____ home now love___ has gone.___ On my pa-ger say-ing...
-ty when you___ page me ev-'ry___ day,___ with oh...

Why don't you call me no more? It was ev-'ry night you were call-ing me be-fore, giv-en half a
Why won't you an-swer my page? It was you who said things were nev-er gon-na change. And it seems like

chance you'd be knock-ing at my door. So tell me what's changed.
late-ly you're act-ing kin-da strange. So tell me what's changed.
(Tell me___ what's___ changed.)

Why don't you give me some time, tell me, 'cause I can't get you out of my mind. But up un-til
Why can't you ev-en pass by, spare some of your time ev-en just to say "Hi". You're not the type of